PRAYER CHANGES THINGS

Prayer Journal

Discovery House is affiliated with Our Daily Bread Ministries, Grand Rapids, Michigan.

Requests for permission to quote from this book should be directed to: Permissions Department, Discovery House, P.O. Box 3566, Grand Rapids, MI 49501, or contact us by e-mail at permissionsdept@dhp.org.

ISBN: 978-1-62707-520-6

Printed in the United States of America

First printing in 2017P

Sitting in a hospital waiting room with my friend as his wife underwent major surgery, I was struggling to find words to comfort him. I wanted to tell him, "The *best* thing we can do is pray," but it came out, "I guess *all* we can do is pray."

What a difference between those two statements! One treats prayer as an exercise in despair, while the other is laced with confidence in a loving Father and His wise purposes. That moment could have been an opportunity for us to renew our trust in our God, but instead it bordered on pointless. Unintentionally I had wandered from the real purpose and privilege of prayer.

PRAYER MATTERS

Few things reflect the wonder of following Christ like the privilege of prayer. Imagine—not only are we invited to bring our needs and concerns to the Creator of the universe, we are encouraged to do so boldly, not as slaves or subjects, but as children of God himself. We are called to prayer in order to connect our hearts with His. The God of heaven and earth actually wants us to talk to Him! Jesus says, "This, then, is how you should pray ..." (Matthew 6:9).

Scripture tells us that Jesus prayed often when He walked upon the earth. Prayer was at the heart of His relationship with His Father, and it was something His disciples asked Him to teach them to do (Luke 11:1). Why? In part, no doubt, because of the impact they saw Jesus' prayer life having on Him and His work. It was that obvious to them that prayer was vital to Jesus.

Hebrews tells us, "Let us then approach God's throne of grace with confidence, so that we may receive mercy and find grace to help us in our time of need" (Hebrews 4:16). Prayer is our opportunity to communicate with the God with whom all things are possible. It is what can bring the light of hope into the darkest of circumstances. It is both *all* we can do, and the *best thing* we can do.

WHERE DO I START?

Because prayer is such a vital part of every Christ-follower's spiritual journey, this prayer journal has been designed to help us cultivate and deepen our prayer lives. It contains important reminders and encouragement to pray, and it provides an opportunity to explore and discover God's great faithfulness as we pray. How?

Here are a few ways to use this tool to enrich your relationship with God by strengthening your prayer life.

First and most obviously, keep a record of the people, needs, relationships, challenges, and circumstances you pray for or about. Allow that record to keep you on track when praying is difficult and focus is a challenge.

Second, occasionally write out your prayers. Take time to think carefully about the need of the moment and your need of God and His provision. Express your confidence in His wisdom and purposes, and thank Him for hearing your prayers.

Third, examine the Scriptures, particularly the psalms, where you find others who have faced similar struggles and felt similar emotions, and allow their words to help you express your heart and concern. When you can't find the words to pray, it can help to pray the prayers of the Bible. You'll find a helpful appendix of prayers in the back of this journal.

Finally, journal about how God has answered your prayers. When His answer aligns with your desire, thank Him for His grace. When He responds in a way that differs from your wishes, express your trust in His wisdom and purposes.

NEW MERCIES

In an Old Testament book filled with lament, we find words of hope. Words of confidence. Words about the character of God. Jeremiah wrote, "Because of the Lord's great love we are not consumed, for his compassions never fail. They are new every morning; great is your faithfulness" (Lamentations 3:22–23).

As you journal your prayer life, time will reveal how true those ancient words really are. Ultimately, prayer matters because of the person to whom we pray. He is our Father in heaven, rich with mercy, unfailing compassion, and great faithfulness—all of which are available to us as we pray.

There is no time like the present. Let's pray and see what God does in us, for us, and through us as we welcome Him into our lives.

Bill Crowder

Cast all your anxiety on him because he cares for you.

1 PETER 5:7

PRAYER CHANGES

PEOPLE

NO NEED IS TOO TRIVIAL

As a father has compassion on his children,
so the LORD has compassion on those who fear him.

PSALM 103:13

Several mothers of small children were sharing encouraging answers to prayer. One woman, however, said she felt selfish about troubling God with her personal needs. "Compared with the huge global needs God faces," she explained, "my circumstances must seem trivial to Him."

Moments later, her little son pinched his fingers in a door and ran screaming to his mother. She didn't say, "How selfish of you to bother me with your throbbing fingers when I'm busy!" She showed him great compassion and tenderness.

As Psalm 103:13 reminds us, this is the response of love, both human and divine. In Isaiah 49, God said that even though a mother may forget to have compassion on her child, the Lord never forgets His children (v. 15). God assured His people, "I have engraved you on the palms of my hands" (v. 16).

Such intimacy with God belongs to those who fear Him and who rely on Him rather than on themselves. As that child with throbbing fingers ran freely to his mother, so may we run to God with our daily problems.

Our compassionate God doesn't neglect others to respond to our concerns. He has limitless time and love for each of His children. No need is too trivial for Him.

Joanie Yoder

In the morning, LORD, you hear my voice;
in the morning I lay my requests before
you and wait expectantly.

PSALM 5:3

This is the confidence we have in approaching God: that if we ask anything according to his will, he hears us.

1 JOHN 5:14

MINDLESS PRAYER

"No one will be able to stand against you all the days of your life. As I was with Moses, so I will be with you; I will never leave you nor forsake you."

JOSHUA 1:5

Sometimes I am ashamed of my prayers. Too often I hear myself using familiar phrases that are more like mindless filler than thoughtful, intimate interaction. One phrase that annoys me, and that I think might offend God, is "Lord, be with me." In Scripture, God has already promised not to leave me.

God made this promise to Joshua just before he led the Israelites into the Promised Land (Joshua 1:5). The author of Hebrews later claimed it for all believers: "Never will I leave you; never will I forsake you" (13:5). In both cases, the context indicates that God's presence has to do with giving us the power to carry out His will, not our own will, which is generally what I have in mind in my prayers.

Perhaps a better prayer would be something like this: "Lord, thank you for your indwelling Spirit who is willing and able to direct me in the ways you want me to go. May I not take you where you don't want to go. May I not enlist you to do my will, but humbly submit to doing yours."

When we are doing God's will, He will be with us even without our asking. If we're not doing His will, we need to ask for His forgiveness, change our course, and follow Him.

Julie Ackerman Link

Do not be anxious about anything, but in every situation, by prayer and petition, with thanksgiving, present your requests to God.

PHILIPPIANS 4:6

Let us then approach God's throne of grace with confidence, so that we may receive mercy and find grace to help us in our time of need.

HEBREWS 4:16

WAITING . . .

Be joyful in hope, patient in affliction, faithful in prayer.

ROMANS 12:12

Day after day for years Harry shared with the Lord his concern for his son-in-law John, who had turned away from God. But then Harry died. A few months later, John did indeed turn back to God. When his mother-in-law Marsha told him that Harry had been praying for him every day, John replied, "I waited too long." But Marsha joyfully shared, "The Lord is still answering the prayers Harry prayed during his earthly life."

Harry's story is an encouragement to us who pray and wait. He continued to be "faithful in prayer" and waited patiently (Romans 12:12).

The author of Psalm 130 experienced waiting in prayer. He said, "I wait for the Lord, my whole being waits" (v. 5). He found hope in God because he knew that "with the Lord is unfailing love and with him is full redemption" (v. 7).

Author Samuel Enyia wrote about God's timing: "God does not depend on our time. Our time is chronological and linear but God . . . is timeless. He will act at the fullness of His time. Our prayer . . . may not necessarily rush God into action, but . . . places us before Him in fellowship."

What a privilege we have to fellowship with God in prayer and to wait for His answer in the fullness of His time.

Anne Cetas

This, then, is how you should pray: "Our Father in heaven, hallowed be your name, your kingdom come, your will be done, on earth as it is in heaven. Give us today our daily bread. And forgive us our debts, as we also have forgiven our debtors. And lead us not into temptation, but deliver us from the evil one."

MATTHEW 6:9–13

Ask and it will be given to you; seek
and you will find; knock and the
door will be opened to you.

MATTHEW 7:7

THE LITTLE TENT

For God was pleased to have
all his fullness dwell in [Jesus].

COLOSSIANS 1:19

During evangelist Billy Graham's historic 1949 Los Angeles campaign, the big tent that held over six thousand people was filled to overflowing every night for eight weeks. Close by was a smaller tent set aside for counseling and prayer. Cliff Barrows, longtime music director and close friend and associate of Graham, has often said that the real work of the gospel took place in "the little tent," where people gathered on their knees to pray before and during every evangelistic service. A local Los Angeles woman, Pearl Goode, was the heart of those prayer meetings and many that followed.

In the apostle Paul's letter to the followers of Christ in Colosse, he assured them that he and his colleagues were praying continually for them (Colossians 1:3, 9). In closing he mentioned Epaphras, a founder of the Colossian church, who is "always wrestling in prayer for you, that you may stand firm in all the will of God" (4:12).

Some people are given the high visibility task of preaching the gospel in "the big tent." But God has extended to all of us, just as He did to Epaphras and Pearl Goode, the great privilege of kneeling in "the little tent" and bringing others before the throne of God.

David McCasland

Cast your cares on the Lord and he will sustain you.

PSALM 55:22

The Spirit helps us in our weakness. We do not know what we ought to pray for, but the Spirit himself intercedes for us through wordless groans.

ROMANS 8:26

IS HE LISTENING?

About three in the afternoon Jesus cried out in a loud voice, "Eli, Eli, lema sabachthani?" (which means "My God, my God, why have you forsaken me?").

MATTHEW 27:46

"Sometimes it feels as if God isn't listening to me." Those words, which were spoken by a woman who tried to stay strong in her walk with God while coping with an alcoholic husband, echo the heart-cry of many believers. For many years, she asked God to change her husband. Yet it never happened.

What are we to think when we repeatedly ask God for something good—something that could easily glorify Him—but the answer doesn't come? Is He listening or not?

Let's look at the life of the Savior. In the garden of Gethsemane, He agonized for hours in prayer, pouring out His heart and pleading, "Let this cup pass from Me" (Matthew 26:39 NKJV). But the Father's answer was clearly "No." To provide salvation, God had to send Jesus to die on the cross. Even though Jesus felt as if His Father had forsaken Him, He prayed intensely and passionately because He trusted that God was listening.

When we pray, we may not see how God is working or understand how He will bring good through it all. So we have to trust Him. We relinquish our rights and let God do what is best.

We must leave the unknowable to the all-knowing One. He is listening and working things out His way.

Dave Branon

Your Father knows what you need before you ask him.

MATTHEW 6:9–13

The prayer of a righteous person is powerful and effective.

JAMES 5:16

PANIC OR PRAY?

Then Asa called to the LORD his God and said, "LORD, there is no one like you to help the powerless against the mighty. Help us, LORD."

2 CHRONICLES 14:11

An eighty-five-year-old woman, all alone in a convent, got trapped inside an elevator for four nights and three days. Fortunately, she had a jar of water, some celery sticks, and a few cough drops. After she tried unsuccessfully to open the elevator doors and get a cell phone signal, she turned to God in prayer. "It was either panic or pray," she later told CNN. In her distress, she relied on God and waited till she was rescued.

King Asa of Judah was also faced with the options of "panic or pray" (2 Chronicles 14). He was attacked by an Ethiopian army of a million men. But as he faced this huge fighting force, instead of relying on military strategy or cowering in dread, he turned to the Lord in urgent prayer. In a powerful and humble prayer, Asa confessed his total dependence on Him, asked for help, and appealed to the Lord to protect His own name: "Help us, LORD our God, for we rely on you, and in your name we have come against this vast army" (v. 11). The Lord responded to Asa's prayer, and Judah won the victory over the Ethiopian army.

When we are faced with tight spots, meager resources, a vast army of problems, or seemingly dead-end solutions, let's not panic. Let's turn to God, who fights for His people and gives them victory.

Marvin Williams

Rejoice always, pray continually,
give thanks in all circumstances.

1 THESSALONIANS 5:16–18

The Lord is near to all who call on him,
to all who call on him in truth.

PSALM 145:18

PRAYER CHANGES

POSSIBILITIES

GOD OF THE ORDINARY

No temptation has overtaken you except what is common to mankind. And God is faithful.

1 CORINTHIANS 10:13

Hearing testimonies about how God did something spectacular in someone else's life can challenge us. Yet while we may rejoice to hear about answers to prayer, we may also wonder why God hasn't done anything amazing for us lately.

It's easy to think that if God showed up in astonishing ways for us as He did for Abraham, then we would be more inspired to be faithful servants of God. But then we remember that God showed up for Abraham only every twelve to fourteen years, so most of Abraham's journey was rather ordinary (see Genesis 12:1–4; 15:1–6; 16:16–17:12).

God's work is usually done behind the scenes in the ordinary things of life. As our text says, "He will not let you be tempted beyond what you can bear. But when you are tempted, he will also provide a way out" (1 Corinthians 10:13). Every day, God shields us from devastating onslaughts of Satan that would otherwise leave us helplessly defeated. And when temptation hits, He is making exit ramps for us so we can escape.

When we put our head on the pillow at night, we should pause to thank God for the amazing things He has done for us that day in the midst of our ordinary lives. So, instead of longing for Him to do something spectacular for you, thank Him! He already has.

Joe Stowell

Devote yourselves to prayer, being watchful and thankful.

COLOSSIANS 4:2

Look to the Lord and his strength; seek his face always.

1 CHRONICLES 16:11

ALWAYS PRAY AND DON'T GIVE UP

Then Jesus told his disciples a parable to show them that they should always pray and not give up.

LUKE 18:1

Are you going through one of those times when it seems every attempt to resolve a problem is met with a new difficulty? You thank the Lord at night that it's taken care of but awake to find that something else has gone wrong and the problem remains.

During an experience like that in my life, I was reading the gospel of Luke and was astounded by the opening words of chapter 18: "Then Jesus told his disciples a parable to show them that they should always pray and not give up" (v. 1). I had read the story of the persistent widow many times but never grasped why Jesus told it (vv. 2–8). Now I connected those opening words with the story. The lesson to His followers was very clear: "Always pray and never give up."

Prayer is not a means of coercing God to do what we want. It is a process of recognizing His power and plan for our lives. In prayer we yield our lives and circumstances to the Lord and trust Him to act in His time and in His way.

As we rely on God's grace not only for the outcome of our requests but also for the process, we can keep coming to the Lord in prayer, trusting His wisdom and care for us.

Our Lord's encouragement to us is clear: Always pray and don't give up!

David McCasland

Be joyful in hope, patient in affliction, faithful in prayer.

ROMANS 12:12

Is anyone among you in trouble? Let them pray.
Is anyone happy? Let them sing songs of praise.

JAMES 5:13

WAITING FOR AN ANSWER

Those who know your name trust in you, for you, Lord, have never forsaken those who seek you.

PSALM 9:10

When our daughter was fifteen, she ran away. She was gone more than three weeks. Those were the longest three weeks of our lives. We looked everywhere for her and sought help from law enforcement and friends. During those desperate days, my wife and I learned the importance of waiting on God in prayer. We had come to the end of our strength and resources. We had to rely on God.

It was on a Father's Day that we found her. We were in a restaurant parking lot, on our way to dinner, when the phone rang. A waitress at another restaurant had spotted her. Our daughter was only three blocks away. We soon had her home, safe and sound.

We have to wait on God when we pray. We may not know how or when He will answer, but we can put our hearts constantly before Him in prayer. Sometimes the answers to our prayers don't come when we would hope. Things may even go from bad to worse. But we have to persevere. That happens as we keep believing and keep asking.

Waiting is never easy, but the end result, whatever it is, will be worth it. David put it this way: "Those who know your name trust in you, for you, LORD, have never forsaken those who seek you" (Psalm 9:10).

Keep seeking. Keep trusting. Keep asking. Keep praying.

James Banks

Answer me when I call to you, my righteous God. Give me relief from my distress; have mercy on me and hear my prayer.

PSALM 4:1

In my distress I called to the Lord; I cried to my God for help. From his temple he heard my voice; my cry came before him, into his ears.

PSALM 18:6

MIRACLE RAIN

Remember the former things, those of long ago; I am God, and there is no other.

ISAIAH 46:9

Life is hard for the villagers who live on a hilly terrain in the Yunnan Province of China. Their main source of food is corn and rice. But in a recent year a severe drought hit the region and the crops withered. Everyone was worried, and many superstitious practices were carried out as the people attempted to end the drought. When nothing worked, people started blaming the five Christians in the village for offending the spirits of the ancestors.

These five believers gathered to pray. Before long, the sky darkened and thunder was heard. A heavy downpour started and lasted the whole afternoon and night. The crops were saved! While most of the villagers did not believe God sent the rain, others did and desired to find out more about Him and Jesus.

In 1 Kings 17 and 18 we read of a severe drought in Israel. But in this case, we are told, it was a result of God's judgment on His people (17:1). They had begun to worship Baal, the god of the Canaanites, believing that this deity could send the rain for their crops. Then God, through His prophet Elijah, showed that He is the one true God who determines when rain falls.

Our all-powerful God desires to hear our prayers and answer our pleas. And though we do not always understand His timing or His purposes, God always responds with His best for our lives.

Poh Fang Chia

The righteous cry out, and the Lord hears them.

PSALM 34:17

Pray in the Spirit on all occasions with all kinds of prayers and requests. With this in mind, be alert and always keep on praying for all the Lord's people.

EPHESIANS 6:18

TIME FOR A CHANGE

From there he went on toward the hills east of Bethel and pitched his tent, with Bethel on the west and Ai on the east.

GENESIS 12:8

Many believers long to spend daily time with God, praying and reading His Word. Ironically, they are often distracted by a busy schedule. Frustrations mount as busyness seems to crowd out an opening in their schedule.

Oswald Chambers has wisely commented on the transforming power of even five minutes in the presence of the Lord. Indeed, even a short time spent in intercession and the Word still has great value: "It is not the thing on which we spend the most time that moulds us, but the thing that exerts the greatest power. Five minutes with God and His Word is worth more than all the rest of the day." Now, it may sound as if Chambers has made an overstatement. Yet powerful results can come from even a short time of prayer, because God is powerful.

Sometimes our days are filled with busy demands that crowd out time spent in listening to and responding to God. But no matter where we are, any time taken to build our own spiritual "altar" to the Lord as Abram did (Genesis 12:8) opens the door to His transforming power. If you are having trouble establishing a time with God, you could start with just five minutes and see where it leads. Our God longs to meet with us and show His power in our lives.

Dennis Fisher

Let us kneel before the Lord our Maker;
for he is our God, and we are the people of
his pasture, the flock under his care.

PSALM 95:6-7

May my prayer be set before you like incense; may the lifting up of my hands be like the evening sacrifice.

PSALM 141:2

THERE'S POWER

Therefore confess your sins to each other and pray for each other so that you may be healed.

JAMES 5:16

When my sister found out she had cancer, I asked my friends to pray. When she had surgery, we prayed that the surgeon would be able to remove all of the cancer and that she wouldn't have to undergo chemotherapy or radiation. And God answered yes! When I reported the news, one friend remarked, "I'm so glad there's power in prayer." I responded, "I'm thankful that God answered with a yes this time."

James says, "the prayer of a righteous person is powerful and effective" (5:16). But does "effective" and "powerful" mean that the harder we pray, or the more people we ask to pray, the more likely God is to answer with a yes? I've had enough "no" and "wait" answers to wonder about that.

Prayer is powerful, but it's such a mystery. We're taught to have faith, to ask earnestly and boldly, to persevere, to be surrendered to His will. Yet God answers in His wisdom and His answers are best. I'm just thankful that God wants to hear our hearts and that no matter the answer, He is still good.

I like Ole Hallesby's words: "Prayer and helplessness are inseparable. Only those who are helpless can truly pray. . . . Your helplessness is your best prayer." We can do helplessness quite well.

Anne Cetas

They raised their voices together in prayer to God. "Sovereign Lord," they said, "you made the heavens and the earth and the sea, and everything in them."

ACTS 4:24

Jesus went out to a mountainside to pray,
and spent the night praying to God.

LUKE 6:12

PRAYER CHANGES

PRIORITIES

ANGRY PRAYERS

Fools give full vent to their rage,
but the wise bring calm in the end.

PROVERBS 29:11

The neighbors probably didn't know what to think as they looked out their windows at me one wintry day. I was standing in the driveway with a garden shovel clutched in my hands, whacking wildly and angrily at a clump of ice that had formed beneath a corner gutter. With each smack, I was uttering prayers that were variations on one theme: "I can't do this." "You can't expect me to do this." "I don't have the strength to do this." As a caregiver, with a long list of responsibilities to handle, I now had this ice to deal with, and I had had enough!

My anger was wrapped around a bundle of lies: "I deserve better than this." "God isn't enough after all." "Nobody cares anyway." But when we choose to cling to our anger, we become mired in the trap of bitterness, never moving forward. And the only cure for anger is truth.

The truth is that God does not give us what we deserve; He gives us mercy instead. "You, Lord, are forgiving and good, abounding in love to all who call to you" (Psalm 86:5). The truth is that God is more than enough, despite what we see. The truth is that His strength is sufficient (2 Corinthians 12:9). Yet before we can find such reassurance, we may need to step back, lay down the shovel of our own efforts, and take Jesus' hand that's extended to us in mercy and grace.

God is big enough to listen to our anger and loving enough to show us—in His time—the path forward.

Shelly Beach

Since we have a great priest over the house of God, let us draw near to God with a sincere heart and with the full assurance that faith brings.

HEBREWS 10:21–22

If you, then, though you are evil, know how to give good gifts to your children, how much more will your Father in heaven give good gifts to those who ask!

MATTHEW 7:11

PRAY FIRST

He inquired of the LORD, saying, "Shall I go and attack these Philistines?"

1 SAMUEL 23:2

When my husband and I supervise our son's piano practice sessions, we begin by asking God to help us. We pray first because neither my husband nor I know how to play the instrument. Together, all three of us are coming to understand musical mysteries such as the meaning of "staccato" and "legato" and when to use the piano's black keys.

Prayer becomes a priority when we realize that we need God's help. David needed God's assistance in a dangerous situation as he considered fighting the Philistines in the city of Keilah. Before engaging in battle, David "inquired of the LORD, saying, 'Shall I go and attack these Philistines?'" (1 Samuel 23:2). God gave His approval. However, David's men admitted that the enemy forces intimidated them. Before a single sword was lifted against the Philistines, David prayed again. God promised him the victory he later claimed (v. 4).

Does prayer guide our lives, or is it our last resort when trouble strikes? We sometimes fall into the habit of making plans and then asking God to bless them, or praying only in moments of desperation. God does want us to turn to Him in moments of need. But He also wants us to remember that we need Him all the time (Proverbs 3:5–6).

Jennifer Benson Schuldt

"Before they call I will answer; while
they are still speaking I will hear."

ISAIAH 65:24

In him and through faith in him we may approach God with freedom and confidence.

EPHESIANS 3:12

A HEART FOR PRAYER

My heart says of you, "Seek his face!"
Your face, LORD, I will seek.

PSALM 27:8

While traveling on an airplane with her four- and two-year-old daughters, a young mom worked at keeping them busy so they wouldn't disturb others. When the pilot's voice came over the intercom for an announcement, Catherine, the younger girl, paused from her activities and put her head down. When the pilot finished, she whispered, "Amen." Perhaps because there had been a recent natural disaster, she thought the pilot was praying.

Like that little girl, I want a heart that turns my thoughts toward prayer quickly. I think it would be fair to say that the psalmist David had that kind of heart. We get hints of that in Psalm 27 as he speaks of facing difficult foes (v. 2). He said, "Your face, LORD, I will seek" (v. 8). Some say that when David wrote this psalm he was remembering the time he was fleeing from Saul (1 Samuel 21:10) or from his son Absalom (2 Samuel 15:13–14). Prayer and dependence on God were in the forefront of David's thinking, and he found Him to be his sanctuary (Psalm 27:4–5).

We need a sanctuary as well. Perhaps reading or praying this psalm and others could help us to develop that closeness to our Father-God. As God becomes our sanctuary, we'll more readily turn our hearts toward Him in prayer.

Anne Cetas

When you pray, go into your room, close the door
and pray to your Father, who is unseen.

MATTHEW 6:6

If my people, who are called by my name, will humble themselves and pray and seek my face and turn from their wicked ways, then I will hear from heaven.

2 CHRONICLES 7:14

OUR PRAYER; GOD'S WILL

Three times I pleaded with the
Lord to take it away from me.

2 CORINTHIANS 12:8

The handwritten prayer request was heartbreaking in its seeming impossibility: "Please pray—I have multiple sclerosis, weak muscles, trouble swallowing, increased pain, diminishing sight." The woman's body was breaking down, and I could sense despair in her plea for intercession.

But then came the hope—the strength that trumps the physical damage and degradation: "I know our blessed Savior is in full control. His will is of utmost importance to me."

This person may have needed my prayers, but I needed something she had: unabated confidence in God. She seemed to present a perfect portrait of the truth God taught Paul when he asked for relief from his difficulty—what he called a "thorn in my flesh" (2 Corinthians 12:7). His quest for relief turned out to be not just a seeming impossibility; his request was turned down flat by his heavenly Father. Paul's continual struggle, which was clearly God's will, was a valuable lesson: Through his weakness, God's grace could be displayed and God's strength was "made perfect" (v. 9).

As we pour out our hearts to God, let's be even more concerned with seeking His will than we are with receiving the answer we want. That's where the grace and the strength come from.

Dave Branon

Then you will call on me and come and
pray to me, and I will listen to you.

JEREMIAH 29:12

One thing I ask from the Lord, this only do I seek: that I may dwell in the house of the Lord all the days of my life, to gaze on the beauty of the Lord and to seek him in his temple.

PSALM 27:4

UNANSWERED

Always pray and [don't] give up.

LUKE 18:1

One of my biggest struggles is unanswered prayer. Maybe you can relate. You ask God to rescue a friend from addiction, to grant salvation to a loved one, to heal a sick child, to mend a relationship. All these things you think must be God's will. For years you pray. But you hear nothing back from Him and you see no results.

You remind the Lord that He's powerful—that your request is a good thing. You plead. You wait. You doubt—maybe He doesn't hear you, or maybe He isn't so powerful after all. You quit asking—for days or months. You feel guilty about doubting. You remember that God wants you to take your needs to Him, and you tell Him your requests again.

We may sometimes feel we're like the persistent widow in Jesus' parable recorded in Luke 18. She keeps coming to the judge, badgering him and trying to wear him down so he'll give in. But we know that God is kinder and more powerful than the judge in the parable. We trust Him, for He is good and wise and sovereign. We remember that Jesus said we "always ought to pray and not lose heart" (v. 1).

So we ask Him, "Summon your power, God; show us your strength, our God, as you have done before" (Psalm 68:28). And then we trust Him . . . and wait.

Anne Cetas

If any of you lacks wisdom, you should ask God, who gives generously to all without finding fault.

JAMES 1:5

I will pray with my spirit, but I will also pray with my understanding;
I will sing with my spirit, but I will also sing with my understanding.

1 CORINTHIANS 14:15

CRUMBS OF TIME

Three times a day [Daniel] got down on his knees and prayed, giving thanks to his God.

DANIEL 6:10

A friend was coming to town. He is a very busy man and his schedule was tight, but after a difficult day in important meetings, he managed to see my family for half an hour for a quick and late dinner. We enjoyed his visit, but I remember looking at my plate and thinking, "We only got the crumbs of his time."

Then I remembered how many times God gets the crumbs of my time—sometimes just the last minutes before I fall asleep.

Daniel was a busy man. He held a high government position in the ancient kingdom of Babylon, and I'm sure he had a full schedule. However, he had developed the habit of spending time with God—praying three times a day, praising God, and thanking Him. This routine helped him develop a strong faith that did not waver when he faced persecution (Daniel 6).

God desires a relationship with us. In the morning we can invite Him into our day, and then we can praise Him and ask Him for His help throughout the day. At other times we can treasure some time alone with Him and reflect on His faithfulness. As we spend time with God in prayer and in His Word, we grow in our relationship with Him and learn to become more and more like Him. As time with God becomes a priority, we enjoy His company more and more.

Keila Ochoa

Watch and pray so that you will not fall into temptation.
The spirit is willing, but the flesh is weak.

MATTHEW 26:41

Make thankfulness your sacrifice to God, and keep the vows you made to the Most High. Then call on me when you are in trouble, and I will rescue you, and you will give me glory.

PSALM 50:14-15 NLT

PRAYER CHANGES

FOCUS

PRAYER MARATHON

Pray continually.

1 THESSALONIANS 5:17

Do you struggle to maintain a consistent prayer life? Many of us do. We know that prayer is important, but it can also be downright difficult. We have moments of deep communion with God, and then we have times when it feels as if we're just going through the motions. Why do we struggle so in our prayers?

The life of faith is a marathon. The ups, the downs, and the plateaus in our prayer life are a reflection of this race. And just as in a marathon we need to keep running, so we keep praying. The point is: Don't give up!

That is God's encouragement too. The apostle Paul said, "pray continually" (1 Thessalonians 5:17), "keep on praying" (Romans 12:12 NLT), and "devote yourselves to prayer" (Colossians 4:2). All of these statements carry the idea of remaining steadfast and continuing in the work of prayer.

And because God, our heavenly Father, is a personal being, we can develop a time of close communion with Him, just as we do with our close human relationships. A. W. Tozer writes that as we learn to pray, our prayer life can grow "from the initial most casual brush to the fullest, most intimate communion of which the human soul is capable." And that's what we really want—deep communication with God. It happens as we keep praying.

Poh Fang Chia

Three times I pleaded with the Lord to take it away from me. But he said to me, "My grace is sufficient for you, for my power is made perfect in weakness."

2 CORINTHIANS 12:8-9

Give attention to your servant's prayer and his plea for mercy, Lord my God. Hear the cry and the prayer that your servant is praying in your presence this day.

1 KINGS 8:28

THE VALLEY OF VISION

When my life was ebbing away,
I remembered you, LORD.

JONAH 2:7

The Puritan prayer "The Valley of Vision" speaks of the distance between a sinful man and his holy God. The man says to God, "Thou hast brought me to the valley of vision . . . ; hemmed in by mountains of sin I behold Thy glory." Aware of his wrongs, the man still has hope. He continues, "Stars can be seen from the deepest wells, and the deeper the wells the brighter Thy stars shine." Finally, the poem ends with a request: "Let me find Thy light in my darkness, . . . Thy glory in my valley."

Jonah found God's glory during his time in the ocean's depths. He rebelled against God and ended up in a fish's stomach, overcome by his sin. There, Jonah cried to God: "You cast me into the deep . . . . The waters surrounded me, even to my soul" (Jonah 2:3, 5 NKJV). Despite his situation, Jonah said, "I remembered you, LORD, and my prayer rose to you" (v. 7). God heard his prayer and caused the fish to free him.

Although sin creates distance between God and us, we can look up from the lowest points in our lives and see Him—His holiness, goodness, and grace. If we turn away from our sin and confess it to God, He will forgive us. God answers prayers from the valley.

Jennifer Benson Schuldt

I cried out to him with my mouth; his praise was on my tongue.

PSALM 66:17

Give thanks to the Lord, for he is good; his love endures forever.

PSALM 107:1

SEEING NEAR AND FAR

The LORD is near to all who call on him,
to all who call on him in truth.

PSALM 145:18

Having two healthy eyes is not enough to see clearly. I know this from experience. After a series of eye surgeries for a torn retina, both eyes could see well but they refused to cooperate with each other. One eye saw things far away and the other saw things close up. But instead of working together, they fought for supremacy. Until I could get new prescription glasses three months later, my eyes remained unfocused.

Something similar happens in our view of God. Some people focus better on God when they see Him as "close up"—when they think of Him as intimately present in their daily life. Other Christians see God more clearly as "far away" or far beyond anything they can imagine, ruling the universe in power and majesty.

While people disagree about which view is best, the Bible works like a prescription lens helping us to see that both are correct. King David presents both views in Psalm 145: "The LORD is near to all who call upon him" (v. 18) and "Great is the LORD, and most worthy of praise; his greatness on one can fathom" (v. 3).

Thankfully, our Father in heaven is near enough to hear our prayers yet so far above us in power that He can meet every need.

Julie Ackerman Link

They devoted themselves to the apostles' teaching and to fellowship, to the breaking of bread and to prayer.

ACTS 2:42

I thank my God every time I remember you.
In all my prayers for all of you, I always pray with joy.

PHILIPPIANS 1:3–4

FIRST RESPONSE

Do not be anxious about anything, but in every situation, by prayer and petition, with thanksgiving, present your requests to God. And the peace of God, which transcends all understanding, will guard your hearts and your minds in Christ Jesus.

PHILIPPIANS 4:6–7

When my husband, Tom, was rushed to the hospital for emergency surgery, I began to call family members. My sister and her husband came right away to be with me, and we prayed as we waited. Tom's sister listened to my anxious voice on the phone and immediately said, "Cindy, can I pray with you?" When my pastor and his wife arrived, he too prayed for us (James 5:13–16).

Oswald Chambers wrote: "We tend to use prayer as a last resort, but God wants it to be our first line of defense. We pray when there's nothing else we can do, but God wants us to pray before we do anything at all."

At its root, prayer is simply a conversation with God, spoken in the expectation that God hears and answers. Prayer should not be a last resort. In His Word, God encourages us to engage Him in prayer (Philippians 4:6). We also have His promise that when "two or three gather" in His name, He will be "with them" (Matthew 18:20).

For those who have experienced the power of the Almighty, the first inclination often will be to cry out to Him. Nineteenth-century pastor Andrew Murray said: "Prayer opens the way for God Himself to do His work in us and through us."

Cindy Kasper

Where two or three gather in my name, there am I with them.

MATTHEW 18:20

I urge, then, first of all, that petitions, prayers, intercession and thanksgiving be made for all people.

1 TIMOTHY 2:1

HEARD BY GOD

Hannah was praying in her heart, and her lips were moving but her voice was not heard.

1 SAMUEL 1:13

After reading several children's books with my daughter, I told her that I was going to read a grown-up book for a while. Later, we would look at books together again. I opened the cover and began to read in silence. A few minutes later, she looked at me doubtfully and said, "Mommy, you aren't really reading." She assumed that since I wasn't speaking, I wasn't processing the words.

Like reading, prayer can be silent. Hannah, who longed for a child of her own, visited the temple and "was praying in her heart" (1 Samuel 1:13). Her lips were moving, but "her voice was not heard." Eli the priest saw her but misunderstood what was happening. She explained, "I was pouring my soul out to the LORD" (v. 15). God heard Hannah's silent prayer request and gave her a son (v. 20).

Since God searches our hearts and minds (Jeremiah 17:10), He sees and hears every prayer—even the ones that never escape our lips. His all-knowing nature makes it possible for us to pray with full confidence that He will hear and answer (Matthew 6:8, 32). Because of this, we can continually praise God, ask Him for help, and thank Him for blessings—even when no one else can hear us.

Jennifer Benson Schuldt

"Call to me and I will answer you and tell you great and unsearchable things you do not know."

JEREMIAH 33:3

I turned to the Lord God and pleaded with
him in prayer and petition.

DANIEL 9:3

HELP NEEDED

Let us then approach God's throne of grace with confidence, so that we may receive mercy and grace to help us in our time of need.

HEBREWS 4:16

During World War II, the British Isles represented the last line of resistance against the sweep of Nazi oppression in Europe. Under relentless attack and in danger of collapse, however, Britain lacked the resources to see the conflict through to victory. For that reason, British Prime Minister Winston Churchill went on BBC radio and appealed to the world: "Give us the tools, and we will finish the job." He knew that without help from the outside, they could not endure the assault they were facing.

Life is like that. Often we are inadequate for the troubles life throws at us, and we need help from outside of ourselves. As members of the body of Christ, that help can come at times from our Christian brothers and sisters (Romans 12:10–13)—and that is a wonderful thing. Ultimately, however, we seek help from our heavenly Father. The good and great news is that our God has invited us to come confidently before Him: "Let us then approach God's throne of grace with confidence, so that we may receive mercy and find grace to help us in our time of need" (Hebrews 4:16).

At such times, our greatest resource is prayer—for it brings us into the very presence of God. There we find, in His mercy and grace, the help we need.

Bill Crowder

Lord, let your ear be attentive to the prayer of this your servant and to the prayer of your servants who delight in revering your name.

NEHEMIAH 1:11

This is my prayer: that your love may abound more and more in knowledge and depth of insight.

PHILIPPIANS 1:9

Be still before the Lord and wait patiently for him.

PSALM 37:7